Donated by

Warren Kump M.D.

© DEMCO, INC. 1990 PRINTED IN U.S.A.

BRITAIN IN PICTURES
THE BRITISH PEOPLE IN PICTURES

BRITISH HOSPITALS

BROTHER JOHN COK, 1392-1468
Initial from the illuminated cartulary of St. Bartholomew's Hospital
written by Brother Cok, 1456-1468

BRITISH HOSPITALS

A. G. L. IVES

WITH
4 PLATES IN COLOUR
AND
26 ILLUSTRATIONS IN
BLACK & WHITE

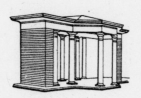

COLLINS · 14 ST. JAMES'S PLACE · LONDON
MCMXLVIII

GENERAL EDITOR
W. J. TURNER

PRODUCED BY
ADPRINT LIMITED LONDON

PRINTED IN GREAT BRITAIN BY
CLARKE & SHERWELL LTD NORTHAMPTON
ON MELLOTEX BOOK PAPER MADE BY
TULLIS RUSSELL & CO LTD MARKINCH SCOTLAND

LIST OF ILLUSTRATIONS

PLATES IN COLOUR

BLACK AND WHITE ILLUSTRATIONS

The Editor is most grateful to all those who have so kindly helped in the selection of illustrations, especially to officials of the various public Museums, Libraries and Galleries, and to all others who have generously allowed pictures and MSS. to be reproduced

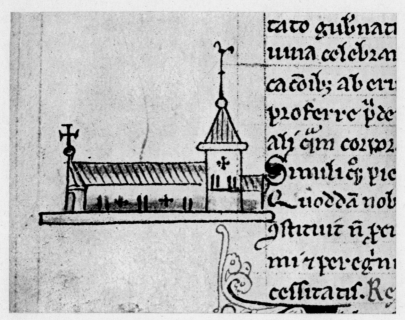

ST. JOHN'S HOSPITAL, OXFORD
Marginal drawing from a fifteenth-century MS.

INTRODUCTORY

THE history of the hospitals in this country is to-day of exceptional
interest. The voluntary and publicly provided hospitals are being
unified in a single system under the technical ownership of the
Ministry of Health. This is an experiment of far-reaching import. To the
popular mind it presents itself in simple terms. The time had come, it was
felt, to have done with the dependence of great hospitals on flag days and
other such uncertain forms of support; the provision of hospitals by the
local authorities had not been an unqualified success, and the burden upon
the rates was excessive. Such was the simple case for the forthright pro-
position of ownership by the State embodied in the National Health Service
Act of 1946.

To anyone with a sense of history, conscious of the extent to which
institutions possess a life of their own moulded by their traditions, the
present experiment offers a rich field for enquiry pregnant with significance
for the immediate future. The experiment now in progress is moreover
unique—a marriage is being attempted between two radically different
traditions. The voluntary hospital tradition is peculiar to this country, to

the Dominions, and to the United States : on the Continent and elsewhere the alternative approach—the provision of hospitals at the expense of the public purse—has, in the absence of a strong voluntary tradition, already occupied the whole field.

Broadly, the history of the hospitals falls into three main phases. The first is that of the foundations of mediæval piety, whilst medicine was still dominated by the outlook of the Church—a phase which lingered on after the suppression of the monasteries by Henry VIII through Tudor and Stuart times. The second phase is that of the growth, mainly in the eighteenth century, of the voluntary hospital as we know it to-day, essentially a partnership between the doctors and enterprising laymen willing to provide the wherewithal for the succour of the sick, so far as their means permitted. Upon this foundation was superimposed, in the middle of the nineteenth century, all that is associated with the name of Florence Nightingale. The third phase is that of the Poor Law institution and its transformation into the public hospital of to-day—a phase whose origin reaches back to Elizabethan times, but which has only emerged as a significant factor in the last two generations. We stand to-day at the beginning of yet another epoch in hospital history, and on the "appointed day" the different streams merge into something new : a phase the significance of which it is only possible to appreciate in the light of the past. What are the elusive factors which decide whether a hospital is but a machine for applying medical techniques to the sick person, or a body corporate providing for those who work in it an opportunity and an inspiration commensurate with the achievements of British medicine? To deal fully with each of these three phases in a brief review such as this is out of the question, but an attempt can be made to notice the features most characteristic of the different streams, and to point to some at least of the factors upon which success or failure will depend.

Even so an apology must be offered for much that receives scant attention in what follows. The account has been deliberately confined to the central stream of hospital development in what is now the commonly accepted sense. Practically the whole story of the extensive mediæval provision for leprosy ; reference to the Plague and to the measures taken to meet it ; reference to smallpox and to Jenner's triumph have all been omitted. So too has the development of the provision for the insane and for infectious diseases, and the provision of hospitals for the armed forces. Even in dealing with the central stream little or no reference has been made to the diets provided at different periods ; to provision for out-patients, vastly important though this aspect of hospital work is ; nor to the extensive provision of "pay-beds" for private patients within the last two generations, and to the development of contributory schemes. To have dealt with all these matters would have overladen the narrative and rendered it a mere catalogue.

A SURGICAL OPERATION AND HEATING THE SURGEON'S INSTRUMENTS
Illumination from *Astronomia Medica*. Early twelfth century

CHRISTIAN PIETY: THE MEDIÆVAL SCENE

THE story of our mediæval hospitals extends over a period of some six and a half centuries, from the Saxon foundations of the ninth and tenth centuries until the suppression of the monasteries by Henry VIII. In England, as elsewhere throughout Christendom, the provision of hospitals for the sick and destitute had long been accepted as an obligation both by the official hierarchy of the Church and by the monastic orders. The "infirmarium" or sickbay was an accepted part of the monastic

9

institution, and merged almost imperceptibly into the "bede-house" whose needy inmates were expected to pray for the souls of the founders. Such institutions must have been numerous from the days of St. Augustine's arrival at Canterbury in 596, and many traces of them still survive. Of hospitals which were not the direct offshoots of monasteries the oldest in Western Europe was the Hôtel Dieu in Paris, founded by the Bishop of Paris in the year 600. The reign of Charlemagne (768-814) was marked by the foundation of hospitals of various kinds all over his vast kingdom, and the movement seems to have spread to Britain, for a Saxon hospital is mentioned at St. Albans in 794 and was followed by others. St. Peter's at York was founded by Athelstan in 937. With the coming of the Normans the establishment of hospitals accompanied the building of castles and cathedrals. Some eight hundred foundations have been listed, and no doubt there were many more, as the list is dependent on the chance survival of written records. It is an astonishing number, comparable with the thousand or so voluntary hospitals existing in this country in recent years.

It is not easy for us moderns with our specialised and secular conception of a hospital to drop back into the earlier Middle Ages and to sense the piety which led to this ample provision. An effort of the imagination is needed to recapture the deeply religious feeling of Catholic Europe with its eyes set towards the Eternal City and the "four last things"—Death, Judgment, Heaven and Hell. Hospitals were founded for the sick, for the feeble and destitute, for the insane and especially for the numerous lepers. Contemporary illustrations show typical structures, sometimes stone, sometimes wood and thatch, often approached through a gatehouse leading to a courtyard : the patients within, propped up in bed, wan and withered, and the attendant figures. Injunctions to religious observances abound in the records of the foundations—chapel bells summoned patients and brethren alike to prayer at intervals throughout the day.

Of the great majority of the eight hundred hospitals our knowledge is scanty, but fortunately there are two famous exceptions. St. Bartholomew's in London can proudly base its history on ancient chronicles of absorbing interest. They record how whilst in Rome on penance in 1123 Rahere, "a courtier though a cleric," was persuaded in a vision "full of truth and sweetness" that he should build a church and priory on the marshy ground of Smithfield. The Norman Church he built of comely stonework still guards his remains. The hospital house he built "a little further off" has survived through the centuries and become the famous hospital it is to-day.

The origins of St. Thomas's fade into legend, but it seems reasonably certain that under the shadow of the Norman priory church of St. Mary Overie (now Southwark Cathedral) there lay an infirmary served by the priory. In 1173 Thomas Becket was canonised, and in 1212 the infirmary which had already become associated with his name was destroyed by fire. The Bishop of Winchester's town house lay near by, and he begged the

LEPER WOMAN RINGING HER BELL
Illumination from the Exeter Pontifical. Late 14th or early 15th century

faithful to give funds for the rebuilding: "Behold at Southwark an ancient spital built of old to entertain the poor has been entirely reduced to cinders and ashes by a lamentable fire." It was separated off as St. Thomas's and rebuilt by 1215 on a new site on the other side of Borough High Street, cheek by jowl with the inns that served sojourners in London and the pilgrims to Canterbury.

On this site stood through the centuries the successive buildings of St. Thomas's Hospital; to-day there remain, easily recognisable, remnants of the hospital buildings left undemolished when during the years 1862-1871 the hospital was transferred to its present site in Lambeth. Both St. Bartholomew's and St. Thomas's were staffed by canons and nuns subject to the Augustinian rule, no doubt assisted by lay brethren and sisters acting as bakers, cooks, nurses and possibly too as surgeons and apothecaries. Their patients suffered from all the ills that afflict mankind, and the very words speak to us across the centuries—"langwissyng men greuyd with variant sorys." One sought "remedie of his akynge hede," another suffered from "bleriednes of yen" (eyes), and yet another from "ryngyng of his erys."

The known history of St. Bartholomew's and St. Thomas's so dominates all that follows that it is easy to forget that in the earlier Middle Ages there were many hospitals of no less importance. In London St. Mary's without Bishopsgate was of equal rank, and its name recurs with the other two until the dissolution of the monasteries. St. Peter's at York was refounded after a fire at St. Leonard's in 1155. It was a large establishment maintaining in 1370 two hundred and twenty-four sick besides orphans and choirboys. There were some two hundred houses for lepers, sixteen of which were dedicated to St. Bartholomew. That at Rochester was probably founded before the year 1100; the Norman chapel still exists in conjunction with a hospital refounded in the nineteenth century. With the decline of leprosy after the middle of the fifteenth century most of the lazar houses fell into decay or were devoted to other purposes. Thus by 1434 at the important hospital of Sherburn near Durham, two places only were kept for lepers, "if they could be found," the hospital being at that date turned over to thirteen destitute men.

The mediæval almshouse is best seen to-day at the Hospital of St. Cross at Winchester, little touched by the passing centuries, and there are many others dotted about the country. St. Mary's at Chichester, to-day an almshouse, originally provided also for the sick. Its great hall with four bays is notable as the finest remaining example of the ancient infirmarium, and its statutes afford a delightful glimpse into the life of the brethren: "if a brother shall have a quarrel with a brother with noise and riot, then let him fast for seven days, on Wednesdays and Fridays, on bread and water, and sit at the bottom of the table and without a napkin . . ." With these few words we must leave the almshouses on one side and return to the central stream to which the word "hospital" came in the course of years to be appropriated.

Miraculous cures of the sick were often recorded and attributed to the invocation of the Saints and to the power of holy relics, but we must beware of supposing that medical science was non-existent. In Franco-Latin Europe of the twelfth and thirteenth centuries there was preserved a genuine remnant of the classical tradition, stifled though it was by the theological assumptions of the age. Away to the south on the shores of the Mediterranean at Salerno there existed a centre of medical learning which traced a direct descent from the Greeks—from Hippocrates and Galen. Though no great advance had been made for a thousand years, a breath of speculative enquiry into the nature of disease still stirred. A little later the Arabian tradition of Averroes and Avicenna reached the west through translations made in Spain, and long dominated the teaching in the schools that were established at Padua and elsewhere. Still to-day we have a vivid reminder of the extent to which this tradition lingers with

MEDIÆVAL SURGICAL TREATMENT
Illustrations to a treatise by John Arderne. 14th century

us in the Arabic symbols used by the medical profession for compounding prescriptions. Clerks in holy orders with a leaning towards medicine betook themselves on lengthy journeys to the south, and returned home to become physicians in the hospitals. By the fourteenth century it is clear that the physician had come to be regarded as essential to the conception of a hospital for the sick, and the distinction between such a hospital and the almshouse for the aged or the destitute was on the way to becoming more clearly defined.

By the fifteenth century, the charitable impulse seems to have faded, and many of the hospitals were the subject of public criticism long before their suppression by Henry VIII. The religious conscience was no longer what it had been in the early flowering of mediæval Europe. Exploitation

13

by those who sought a comfortable retreat at the expense of the charity, whether as incumbents or as privileged patients, seems to have been common, and the flow of fresh endowments was insufficient to compensate for the changing social conditions and the gradual depreciation of existing assets. From about 1400 onwards, a new spirit is evident : the break-up of the feudal system and the growth of the new towns had brought with them the beginnings of the sense of civic responsibility extending to the care of the sick, a spirit which a century later was to prove the only bulwark against the depredations of Henry VIII. It is tempting to speculate how much the decline of the religious hospitals was due to a new attitude on the part of the medical profession. Were they increasingly critical of the limitations imposed upon free enquiry in the hospitals most closely associated with the church, and did they prefer to seek an independent livelihood among the townspeople ? It is perhaps significant that the granting of charters to the Royal College of Physicians and the Company of Barber Surgeons was to coincide with the drive against the hospitals.

In the year 1534 Henry VIII broke with the Pope. The Court and the great merchant community of the towns, if not the older England of the countryside, became aggressively Protestant, and Thomas Cromwell embarked on his famous series of statutes (1536-1547) for the suppression of the religious houses. It was impossible that the hospitals should be exempted, for they were first and foremost religious houses. A statute of 1545 rehearses the fact that "governors and wardens of hospitals, or the greatest number of them, did not exercise due authority and expend the revenues in alms according to the foundation." The object of the Act was "to bring them into a more decent and convenient order." Throughout the transaction a fiction was maintained that Henry would not suffer "poor and miserable people to be unrelieved" ; and in view of the evidence of popular feeling on the subject, it seems credible that the division of the spoils among the King's followers may in fact have been something of an afterthought—a lapse in execution rather than a deliberate fraud upon the people. The fact remains that the great majority of the hospitals were surrendered, saving only some administered by a municipality or closely associated with a cathedral church. The great St. Leonard's at York became a minor charity for thirty-one poor persons. All those connected with the monasteries disappeared. In London, St. Bartholomew's was "vacant and altogether destitute of a master and all fellows and Brethren." St. Thomas's suffered likewise. The idea of Becket as a saint did not appeal to Henry. "Nothing in his life," he said, "whereby he should be called a saint, but rather a rebel and traitor to his Prince."

The lack of hospitals was intolerable to the citizens of London. Sir Richard Gresham, the Lord Mayor, petitioned the King that the city might have the governance of three hospitals—St. Bartholomew's, St. Thomas's and St. Mary's of Bethlehem. They were needed for the "ayde and comforte of the poore, sykke, blynde, aged and impotent persones, being not hable to helpe theymselffs nor havying any place certeyn wheryn they may be lodged, cherysshed and refreshed tyll they be cured and holpen of theyre dyseases and syknesse." The poor, they said, should be helped "frankly and freely by phisicions surgeons appotycaryes, whiche shall have stypende, salary and wages." St. Bartholomew's was refounded by Henry VIII as his own foundation in 1546. Nevertheless the churches, streets and lanes were daily filled with "sick and infirm poor men lying begging." It was the fact that the refounded St. Bartholomew's could not receive a tenth of them that inspired Bishop Ridley to urge upon Edward VI the propriety of refounding "the late hospital of Thomas Becket in Southwark." In 1552 St. Thomas's was re-opened as "The King's Hospital in Southwark." In the new hospital there was for many years a "night lodgers' ward" into which the hospitaller admitted such cases as he deemed deserving. St. Mary's of Bethlehem was given to the City as a house of reception for the insane—more familiar to us as Bedlam. Two other great hospitals were founded in 1553—Christ's Hospital for orphans, and Bridewell as a house of correction. These five rank as Royal Hospitals by virtue of the terms of their refoundation, but would be more properly classified as civic hospitals, owing their existence to the citizens of London rather than to the King.

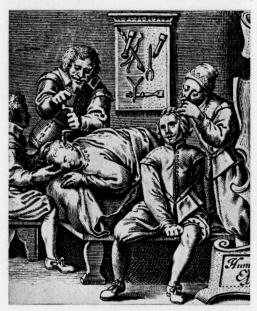

AN OPERATION IN THE SEVENTEENTH CENTURY
Detail from the title page of Ambroise Paré's translated *Workes*, 1649

15

THE ROYAL HOSPITALS
AND THE DAWN OF SCIENTIFIC MEDICINE

IT is impossible to grasp the significance of the dissolution of the old monastic hospitals and the refoundation of St. Bartholomew's and St. Thomas's on a secular basis without an appreciation of the profound change which the Renaissance had wrought in medicine. We are in a different world. The Greek tradition is no longer dimly apprehended, but is now a wide open book. Men of learning and distinction, among them Linacre, founder of the Royal College of Physicians, translated the original Greek. In 1542 Copernicus challenged the Ptolemaic system: in the same year Vesalius of Padua prepared at Basel the skeleton of a criminal and wrote his epoch-making *Fabrica*, which revolutionised the study of anatomy. Dissection of the human body was still difficult and infrequent, but what was undertaken was inspired by a new spirit of open-minded enquiry. In all the universities of Europe questions were being asked and scientific surgery was being born. The narrow horizons of the Middle Ages had gone, never to return.

It is against this background of ferment in medicine that we must see the efforts of the citizens of London to re-establish hospitals under charter from the King. A new model had to be evolved, prototype of the hospital organisation of to-day. A Treasurer was appointed and a group of citizens acted as governors or "almoners," meeting in Committee as members of the City companies had long been accustomed to do for the transaction of business. From the first they conceived it their duty to exercise active supervision over the domestic arrangements generally, and over the Matron and her nurses. A little book was issued by the Lord Mayor describing the new constitution of St. Bartholomew's and containing the charges of the various officials. The sisters were to keep the poor in their diseases sweet and clean—"also ye shall use to them good and honest talke, such as may comfort and amende them." The surgeons were to do their utmost for the

16

patients, "setting aside all fauoure, affection, gayne or lucre." Here already was the great tradition of our hospitals clearly taking shape.

At St. Thomas's hospital one of the almoners always attended at meal times to see that "rations were ample and properly cooked." Surgeons enjoyed a new freedom. They were non-resident, they were remunerated for their services, and they seem to have achieved from this period what we should now term a professional status. The first physician was not appointed at the new St. Thomas's until 1556, when we read that he was to act "at the instruction of the Surgenttes." St. Thomas's was at this time the larger hospital, containing no less than two hundred and sixty beds, whilst St. Bartholomew's, though intended to provide a hundred beds, in fact fell below that number.

Between the refoundation of the Royal Hospitals and the first breath of the new voluntary hospital movement of the eighteenth century with which the next section is concerned, there is a gap of some two hundred years. All through the seventeenth century no important hospitals for the sick existed in England except St. Bartholomew's and St. Thomas's, and the two hospitals carried between them the whole burden of caring for the sick of London. The pressure upon their resources was such that the incurable had to give way to the curable. The abstract of orders for St. Thomas's for the year 1700 specifically records "No incurables are to be received." No history of the hospitals in this country can be satisfactory if it does not pause for a moment and ask why this was so. The charitable spirit flowed in other directions. Many schools now famous were founded at this time, and innumerable almshouses, of which Archbishop Whitgift's foundation at Croydon is a lovely example. The study of medicine flourished in the scientific atmosphere of the age, and was at once rewarded by William Harvey's discovery of the circulation of the blood ; he was at the time physician of St. Bartholomew's though he had been a pupil of Fabricius at Padua. Thomas Sydenham came a little later—a name almost unknown outside medical circles, but one which deserves to be remembered for the transformation he wrought upon the outlook on "fevers."

PROSPECT OF ONE OF THE WARDS OF GUY'S HOSPITAL
Engraving by Thomas Bowles, 1725

17

Neither Church nor State, neither the vigorous citizen bodies of the towns nor wealthy individuals, chose to found hospitals for the sick in England. There is no really satisfying explanation. It has been suggested that perhaps the new medical profession frowned upon the hospitals and preferred to keep such surgery as was undertaken in its own hands. But the explanation does not ring true. The point is surely worthy of serious study by historians for the light it will throw upon those fundamental impulses which determine the form of the social structure. Here one can do no more than record the fact, and suggest that perhaps a clue may be found in a loss of confidence in the old-style apothecary and the fact that physicians and surgeons of the new school were few and far between.

It was not till the close of the century that the mediæval buildings of St. Thomas's were replaced. At St. Bartholomew's rebuilding was postponed until well into the eighteenth century. The new buildings when they came were magnificent. The work was entrusted to James Gibbs, and his original ward blocks grouped round the famous quadrangle with the Great Hall and staircase are yet there to show how a great architect can erect a building suitable for the purpose at any period.

It is convenient to notice here the foundation of Guy's. Thomas Guy was a prominent governor of St. Thomas's Hospital, and his first intention was to provide a magnificent extension to St. Thomas's on the other side of St. Thomas's Street. Finally it emerged as a separate foundation, opened in 1725 with four hundred and thirty-five beds. Much of the original hospital he built still stands, though sadly damaged in 1940-1. His great endowment and the circumstances of its foundation place Guy's rather in the category of the Royal Hospitals than among the voluntary hospitals of the succeeding epoch.

Guy seems to have intended that his hospital should provide for cases which we should now call the "chronic sick," and to some extent for the mentally deranged. The project was found to be unworkable; in 1732 the governors defended their policy by reprinting Guy's will and adding "He himself apprehended, and his suspicions were confirmed by those he consulted, that the word 'Incurable' was of too large and indefinite a significa-tion ; and indeed, people generally understood by it such as laboured under distempers, loss of limbs, blindness and other natural and accidental deformities, and even age itself. And if taken in such an extensive sense, his Hospital must soon have become an Almshouse in which (to use his own words) Parishes as well as individuals would shift off from themselves their dependants and indigent relations . . . and accordingly he described the persons for whose relief he designed the hospital, to be such as were capable of relief by Physick and Surgery." Guy's thus became a hospital for the acute sick in the accepted sense, and its work ran parallel with that of St. Thomas's and St. Bartholomew's.

THE QUADRANGLE OF ST. THOMAS'S HOSPITAL IN 1858

Water colour by T. H. Shepherd

THE VOLUNTARY HOSPITALS
OF THE EIGHTEENTH CENTURY

A WHOLE group of voluntary hospitals were founded in the middle years of the eighteenth century, and to these years the voluntary hospitals proper trace their origin. The political disturbance and intense religious ferment of Puritan times were now but a memory. London had undergone a great change—had more than doubled in size, trade flourished again and the joint stock companies began to assume a new importance in the national life. In England under Queen Anne and the early Georges, men began to think along lines which belong to our own epoch. We can understand their ways of thought and their reactions to the problems of the time. The desire to do something practical in relief of their fellow men, and to do it themselves; the readiness to accept responsibility rather than to petition the King or the Corporation—this was the soil in which there was to grow the voluntary hospital movement which for two hundred years would rank as a leading characteristic of the social structure of the English-speaking peoples.

The movement sprang from small beginnings. The Royal College of Physicians paved the way by encouraging its members to give when desired "gratuitous advice to the sick poor in their localities in London and seven miles around"—advice which may be regarded as the first conscious expression of the theory of professional obligation which made the voluntary hospital movement a possibility. In 1714 John Bellers of the Society of Friends advocated the erection of hospitals for the sick. He, in common with others of his day, had been brought into contact with the Netherlands, whence William of Orange and his Court had journeyed to England. He had been deeply impressed by what he had seen. Over the sea no Henry VIII had despoiled the hospitals. The Englishman is apt to forget that on the Continent many great hospitals—like the ancient Hôtel Dieu at Paris— stood witness to the traditions of Catholic Europe, whilst in the Netherlands former Catholic foundations were flourishing under Protestant administration. Bellers drew his ideas "from a comparison of all the hospitals" of Holland. They covered a wide range of beneficent activities for sick and needy persons. The lack of hospitals was a reproach to England and to her Protestantism. The theme recurs in the first report of the hospital at Winchester twenty-two years later, where mention is made of "a charity which is the glory of other countries and has long been the reproach of our own." The example of the Dutch found a ready welcome among low churchmen and dissenters intent upon good works.

The pride of place belongs to the Westminster Hospital, founded in 1720 in Petty France: "we whose names are underwritten, in obedience to the rules of our holy religion, desiring so far as in us lies to find some

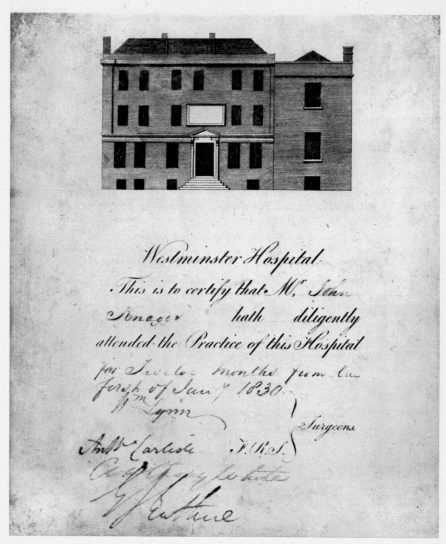

Westminster Hospital

This is to certify that M.ʳ John
Knagg hath diligently
attended the Practice of this Hospital
for Twelve months from the
first of Jan.ʸ 1830

W.ᵐ Lynn

Surgeons

An.ᵗʰ Carlisle F.R.S.

MEDICAL STUDENT'S ATTENDANCE CERTIFICATE

remedy for this great misery of our poor neighbours, do subscribe . . ."
Henry Hoare the banker and Samuel Wesley, a master at Westminster
School and elder brother of John Wesley, were leading spirits in the enter-
prise. It was intended not only to receive patients for a month at a time,
but to allow relief to those incapable of being removed from their homes.

Each subscriber could have one in-patient and one out-patient on the books at the same time: incurables and those suffering from infectious diseases such as small-pox were excluded. When the time came to build a larger hospital, some of the supporters of the Westminster venture felt that the old neighbourhood was not healthy. A split occurred and the dissentients secured a lease of Lanesburgh House in Hyde Park Corner, "a red brick mansion with stables and other outhouses," and so founded St. George's Hospital in 1733. St. George's soon captured the support of the Court and the leaders of society—the names of Lord Chesterfield, Sir Robert Walpole, David Garrick and Beau Nash appear on the early subscription lists.

Another group, meeting in a tavern in Cheapside, took a small house in Featherstone Street in 1740 at a rent of £16 a year, and thus founded the London Hospital. The physician, surgeon and apothecary were to attend from eight to ten on summer mornings and from nine to eleven in winter.

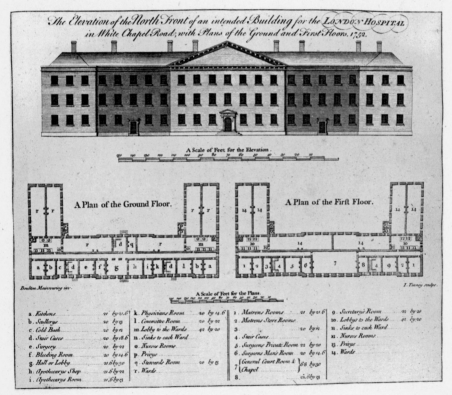

THE LONDON HOSPITAL

Engraving by I. Tinney of the elevation and plans designed by Boulton Mainwaring, 1752

21

THE ENTRANCE TO GUY'S HOSPITAL
Nineteenth-century engraving by W. Woolnoth

A man and his wife were engaged to carry out all the other duties considered necessary. A committee was chosen to meet at the hospital itself every Thursday "to inspect and examine into the management of it." Nurses began to be employed soon afterwards—the first was paid 5s. a week and lived out; a night nurse, known as a "watch," was also engaged at 3s. 6d. a week. Henceforward, there was hardly a meeting but some nurse or watch was dismissed for drunkenness or rebuked for receiving tips from the patients, and the committee advertised for "a sober, grave person who is capable of acting as a nurse." We see too the beginnings of the medical school. Permission was given for a "pupil of surgery" to be entered on the books. He was to have a certificate at the end of the year signifying his attendance. By 1751 the whole scale of the undertaking had so far advanced that a Building Committee had been formed, and part of the present site in Whitechapel secured on lease from the City. Plans were drawn up for a central block with two wings, to accommodate three hundred and fifty beds, though actually only a hundred and sixty-one were provided to begin with. These plans for the original building—still the core of the well-known frontage in Whitechapel Road—are of great interest; they might almost be those of a suburban hospital of to-day. The history of the Middlesex Hospital is similar to that of the London Hospital. It was founded in 1745 to provide for the sick and lame in two small houses close to Tottenham Court Road. Ten years later a great hospital was built which survived until it was rebuilt in the 1930's.

THE MIDDLESEX HOSPITAL
Nineteenth-century engraving after T. H. Shepherd

Meantime away to the north, in overcrowded, precipitous Edinburgh, an inspiration derived from different sources had been at work. Returning home from the great Dutch university of Leiden, then at the height of its prestige as a centre of medical advance, a small group of physicians and surgeons had not only persuaded the university to establish a Faculty of Medicine, but had conceived the idea of founding a hospital where medicine might be practised at the bedside. Their appeal for public subscription met with response sufficient to justify them in taking a little house in the Cowgate and equipping it for the reception of six patients. On the 6th August, 1729, it was ready—"being the First Hospital of that kind that ever was in Scotland." There were at first no nurses, only a housekeeper and one servant. The one rule that governed admission was that the patients must be genuinely poor, and they came from far afield. The Fellows of the College of Physicians "attended in their turns for the space of a fortnight"; the surgery was entrusted to Alexander Monro and five others who undertook to dispense medicines gratis from their shops. Soon the visiting staff were finding it difficult to examine the sick and perform operations on account of the numbers of students who appeared on the scene. The Managers, among whom were now included persons holding office in civic life, were prompted to enlarge the scale of the undertaking, and a Royal Charter was obtained in 1736. In the same year another little hospital was opened by the Incorporation of Surgeons in College Wynd, but before long it was transferred to the Managers of the Infirmary. There followed the purchase of a

THE ROYAL INFIRMARY, SHEFFIELD
Engraving by F. Jukes, 1745-1812

historic site formerly owned by the Black Friars and bounded by the Flodden Wall. "We have got a plan for our house," wrote in his diary George Drummond, six times Lord Provost of Edinburgh, "it is to hold about two hundred patients. We propose to build so much of it as will accommodate sixty-six and five cells for lunatics . . ." The latter provision was prompted by the entire absence in Scotland of any provision for the insane. The new buildings were opened in 1741, care being taken to restrict the number of patients to accord with the interest from the invested capital.

Soon the school became famous. When the disturbance of the Jacobite rising of the '45 had passed away, Edinburgh offered a combination of university education with clinical instruction in the hospital not then available elsewhere in Britain. "The Scottish capital became the new medical Mecca," writes the able historian of the Infirmary, "supplanting and finally eclipsing Leiden." Englishmen outnumbered Scots among the graduates. At Philadelphia, where the first medical school was created in 1765, above the entrance of the medical buildings there is still blazoned the thistle, the emblem of its debt to the country of its parent institution. More than half a century later the great medical faculty of McGill University in Montreal was to owe its origin mainly to a group of Edinburgh graduates. "Thus the great spirit of medicine, revived at the Renaissance at Bologna and Padua and borne across the Alps to Leiden and Edinburgh, spread overseas to enrich the medical schools of the New World."

But we are anticipating, and must return southward and watch the influence of the Westminster example spread far and wide throughout the cities and the larger towns of the kingdom, creating hospitals whose very

24

THE SURGEONS' HALL, EDINBURGH, BUILT IN 1697
Eighteenth-century water colour by an unknown artist

names have become household words and deserve to be recorded for the part they have played in the social history of two hundred years :

Royal Hampshire County Hospital, Winchester	1736	Staffordshire General Infirmary	1766
Bristol Royal Infirmary	1736	Salisbury General Infirmary	1767
York County Hospital	1741	Leeds General Infirmary	1767
Aberdeen Royal Infirmary	1742	Lincoln County Hospital	1769
Royal Devon & Exeter Hospital	1743	Radcliffe Infirmary, Oxford	1770
Northampton General Hospital	1743	Leicester Royal Infirmary	1771
Royal Salop Infirmary, Shrewsbury	1745	Norfolk & Norwich Hospital	1772
		Birmingham General Hospital	1779
Worcester Royal Infirmary	1746	Royal Lancaster Infirmary	1781
Liverpool Royal Infirmary	1749	Nottingham General Hospital	1782
Royal Victoria Infirmary, Newcastle-upon-Tyne	1751	Hull Royal Infirmary	1784
		Durham County Hospital	1793
Manchester Royal Infirmary	1752	Kent & Canterbury Hospital	1793
Gloucestershire Royal Infirmary	1755	Glasgow Royal Infirmary	1794
Chester Royal Infirmary	1761	Belfast Royal Victoria Hospital	1797
Addenbrooke's Hosp., Cambridge	1766	Sheffield Royal Infirmary	1797
		Dundee Royal Infirmary	1798

By 1825 no less than a hundred and twenty-four hospitals and dispensaries had been established. Of these, ten hospitals were in London, seventy-nine in the provinces and ten in Scotland—the remainder being dispensaries. The first voluntary hospitals in Wales were at Denbigh (1807) and Swansea (1817). As yet maternity cases were excluded from the general hospitals. In 1739 twenty-five beds were provided for lying-in women in a house next door to his own by Sir Richard Manningham, the leading obstetrician of his time. From this venture sprang Queen Charlotte's Hospital (so named many years later). The Rotunda in Dublin dates from 1745; others soon followed both in London and elsewhere and became part and parcel of the eighteenth-century hospital movement.

The approach in the towns differed from that of the earlier humbler ventures of the capital. Prominent local people, the clergy and physicians and surgeons, took the movement into their hands and their subscription lists included the aristocracy of the neighbourhood. Their example was in turn followed by the London pioneers when they embarked on their more ambitious building projects. The stories of their beginnings that lie buried in dusty tomes on library shelves take the reader deep into the life of the eighteenth century. A few examples must suffice to indicate the wealth of the material. At Bristol on December 2nd, 1737, the Mayor and Aldermen met at the house they had hired as an Infirmary, and after hearing an excellent sermon repaired to the Nagg's Head Tavern in Wine Street, where they dined together and "finished the day midst the smoke of tobacco, and in emptying and replenishing mugs of fat Bristol ale." The dinners continued but later degenerated and ceased for the good reason that people did not choose to have their heads broken. "Heads broke?" "Yes, Sir, latterly there was such bickering and quarrelling that one was afraid to go without a good cane. . . ." Thirty-four in-patients were admitted, and Visitors were appointed to look after "The House," as most of the early hospitals were called. Above each bed was placed a card, written by the Apothecary, with the name of the patient, the trustee who recommended the case for admission, and the physician or surgeon in charge, together with the diet. The whole of the staff met on Saturdays, "to direct for all the in-patients." In later years the disciples of John Wesley obtained a great following among the patients, and one evening the Apothecary heard a hymn being loudly sung in one of the wards when the inmates should have been settling down for the night. This had to be stopped, but the religious atmosphere long remained, and Bibles were kept on a stand in each ward.

We hear that the ordinary dress of the medical man was a light drab coat, a large wig, a close stock buckled round the neck, black silk stockings, and square-toed shoes with small silver buckles. The students went about in red cloaks and swords—"Better not get too near the curtains, Sir; perhaps that flaming dress of yours may set the bed on fire!"

Exeter was not far behind Bristol, and success there was dramatic. Two patients who had been carried in already laid in their coffins recovered and were able to leave the hospital carrying their shells on their backs! At Worcester the infirmary owed its inception to Bishop Maddox, who had already preached sermons on behalf of the London Hospital and the Westminster. "Few cures," he urged, "are wrought by drugs alone. Proper food, due regimen, necessary attendance, and above all, ease and tranquillity

BRISTOL ROYAL INFIRMARY IN 1742
Engraving by W. H. Tims after W. Halfpenny

of mind have a large share in every recovery." A house in Silver Street taken for a hospital and so used for twenty-five years is still standing and has recently been traced. It was succeeded by a solid building in the Georgian style later to be linked with the name of Sir Charles Hastings, founder of the British Medical Association.

In some cases men who had studied surgery under the inspiration of John Hunter carried back to their own cities the realisation of the need. Thus at Manchester, then a place of some 27,000 inhabitants, Charles White called the citizens together in the Old Coffee House in June, 1752 ; a house was taken in Garden Street, Withy Grove, and twelve beds opened. At Leeds, then a little larger than Manchester, William Hey was the leading spirit. The house rented as a hospital was soon exchanged for a substantial building on the site of the Yorkshire Penny Bank. Hey's fame as a surgeon spread far and wide and was bound up with that of the Infirmary he had created. At Newcastle too, the initiative came from the medical men, stirred by the success achieved elsewhere. "Why then," asked a letter to the *Newcastle Courant*, "do we not follow the laudable example set us lately at Northampton, Worcester, Norwich and other places. . . . By what I can learn, 500 *l.* per year, after the first expense of building will at least maintain forty patients." The infirmary of 1758 must have seemed a strangely modern edifice against the background of the old fortified town, where the walls had only a few years earlier been put into a defensible condition against Charles Edward, the Young Pretender.

Glasgow comes relatively late on the list. The old Royal Infirmary that many still recall was erected amid scenes of much enthusiasm. The brothers Adam were the architects of the finely proportioned buildings, which contained from the start a hundred and thirty-six beds and an operation room accommodating two hundred students.

> "Not planned for idle form and show,
> But to alleviate human woe,"

A Ward in the Middlesex Hospital
Detail from an engraving in Rowlandson and Pugin's *Microcosm of London*, 1808

ran the words of an anthem composed for the occasion. The sentiment was singularly appropriate to a hospital which seventy years later was to be the scene of Lister's demonstration of antiseptic surgery.

In very few of the early hospitals was there any limitation to folk of the locality. Thus at Liverpool the charity was designed to extend to "the many objects that appeared in distress from all parts of the nation and Ireland." Note the use of the word "objects" in reference to the patients : there is no need to suppose that it carried any derogatory sense. In our own hospitals to-day we still talk of "the patient" in a strange impersonal way when we might equally well refer to him and her by name, and years hence our own usage may seem as quaint as the word "object" does to-day. Nevertheless a note of condescension does creep in : we hear reference to the erection of "a spacious and commodious edifice which is now offered to the public, upon whose benevolence and voluntary subscription the extent of its use and service must entirely depend." It is the atmosphere of the elegant Georgian house rather than of the pious founders of the Westminster.

The movement was, as Trevelyan has observed, the means by which the Age of Philanthropy gave solid expression to its feelings, just as the Age of

RAHERE WARD, ST. BARTHOLOMEW'S HOSPITAL
Water colour by an unknown artist, 1832

Faith had sung its soul in the stones of cloisters and cathedral aisles. The fact of its dependence on voluntary support led to a form of organisation which offered freedom to the medical men who worked in the hospitals and enabled them to bring pressure at first hand upon those responsible for policy and finance. As in the case of so many British institutions, the secret was found almost by accident. Surprisingly, the system worked and in the following century outdistanced its continental competitors in the magnitude of its achievements.

But all was not well with those hospitals of the eighteenth and early nineteenth century. Far from it. Looking back to-day we can see the deficiencies readily enough. In the 1780's John Howard, better known as the advocate of prison reform, visited hospitals spreading everywhere his gospel of cleanliness: "My name is Howard, sir. Look into that ward and tell me if it is as it ought to be." He condemned the raising of dust in the wards, and urged that bedding be washed and dried in the sun and then baked. He was far in advance of his time. The character of many ailments was simply not understood. Medical and surgical cases were not separated and right on into the early years of the last century highly infectious fevers, even cholera, were introduced into the hospital wards. Recognition of the grave danger of cross-infection is indeed a process which has not yet worked itself out, and interesting developments are still to-day taking place in the children's hospitals in an effort finally to overcome this age-old curse.

It is, moreover, essential to realise how little the hospitals of the day affected ordinary life in the eighteenth century. A curious sidelight upon the state of popular medicine is afforded by John Wesley's *Primitive Physic*, a handbook first published in 1747, of which twenty-nine editions had been published by 1820. "As theories increased," said the preface, "simple medicines were more and more disregarded." An abundance of new ones had been introduced by reasoning speculative men, yet there had not been wanting some who had endeavoured to explode out of the practice of medicine all the hypotheses and fine-spun theories and to make it a plain intelligible thing. Such a man, commented Wesley, had been the great and good Dr. Sydenham, who had pointed out simple medicines for many diseases. *Primitive Physic* was in the tradition of the herbalists, but was shot through with a strong common-sense insistence on simple food, temperance, cleanliness, fresh air and exercise. We must recognise that it was from this source rather than from the hospitals of the day that there sprang a widespread improvement in the standard of health of the ordinary people. It was a Methodist convert of John Wesley who in 1746 founded the Lock Hospital for venereal diseases near Hyde Park Corner. His action was a direct outcome of the "illiberal rules" of the general hospitals which excluded even innocent victims. This hospital was the pioneer of all curative work in venereal diseases in Great Britain. It was a Quaker tea merchant of York who established a "retired habitation" for the insane where gentle methods displaced the crude restraints of Hogarthian Bedlam. "The Retreat," as it was called was founded in 1792 and carried much farther a movement for the more humane treatment of mental illness which had been begun by St. Luke's in London in 1751.

We must notice too how completely the older mediæval conception of a hospital as a place of refuge for all the sick and destitute had been abandoned, and how in its place had grown up almost a new meaning of the very word "hospital"—now a hospital was to be for the reception of such as were capable of cure by medicine or surgery. To-day we are perceptibly returning to the mediæval conception—dissatisfied with relegating tne "chronic" and the aged to the care of the Poor Law, we are seeking ways and means of broadening the basis of hospital services.

As the Georgian era moved on towards the early Victorian, voices were raised to query in all seriousness the value of the hospitals. Was not mortality greater among the inmates than among those who remained outside? "Until the middle of the nineteenth century," wrote Florence Nightingale many years later, "the organisation and management of hospitals and the nursing of the sick in Britain and most parts of Europe were, except in some few instances, extremely defective."

FLORENCE NIGHTINGALE IN A WARD OF THE HOSPITAL AT SCUTARI
Detail from an engraving from *The Illustrated London News*, February 24th, 1855

1850—THE NIGHTINGALE ERA

IT is now just a hundred years since a leg was first amputated under ether in University College Hospital, London, and it was a year later that Simpson demonstrated his discovery of chloroform as an anæsthetic: "This is far better and stronger than ether." Within twenty years Lister had used carbolic acid as an antiseptic dressing for wounds at the Royal Infirmary in Glasgow, and had embarked on the long struggle before his discovery was accepted. In 1851 Miss Nightingale set out for Kaiserswerth in Germany to learn from the Deaconesses there all that they could tell her of nursing, and in October 1854 she left for the Crimea. The story has often been told of her dramatic use of the power of her personality and her "soft, silvery voice" to rout officialdom and transform the medical organisation of the hospitals at Scutari. Before such events the historian stands abashed; to dwell upon the details would be to destroy all proportion in an account such as this.

Without a sense of the contrast with what had gone before it is impossible to grasp the significance of what had happened. Stowed away in odd corners of our older hospitals there are still to be seen by the curious the old wooden tables and the instruments used by the surgeons, grim relics of the days when a hospital was a place of fear. The ordeal of operation over, the patient faced another equally grim. Back again in the ward he knew well enough that it was touch and go whether the wound could be induced to heal or whether he would succumb in the process. Fevers and grievous stinking sores lay in the beds to right and left. His chief hope was that he, or his friends or relations, would succeed in tipping the women who too often acted as nurses and watches enough to ensure that he did not lack for water or something stronger with which to deaden the pain, and to fend off the prospect of misery from day to day. The nurses were untrained and frequently illiterate. "Wanted," read an advertisement many years later, "a nurse who can read and write, or at least read writing." Beyond keeping the wards clean as far as might be, and the beds tidy, attending to the wants of the patients, serving meals, and maintaining order, her duties consisted chiefly of giving out medicines, making poultices or applying leeches.

It is indeed astonishing that the surgeons achieved any success at all under such conditions, but the old order books with their purchases of wooden legs attest their success. From the 1780's onward things had begun to mend a little and Howard's insistence on cleanliness had brought a measure of order into life in the wards; but the surgery continued to be crude and painful beyond our present comprehension.

As we approach the 1850's the scene changes. Candles had given place to gas jets for lighting in the wards. Baths, drains and "hoists" were arranged. A little notebook started by a doctor in 1853 has recently come to light, and has been described by Sir Arthur Hall. Counting the pulse or the respiration was then and for many years to come entirely a matter for the doctor. "Taking a temperature" was unknown even to the doctor. In the 1860's Sir Clifford Allbutt, then at Leeds, got a local firm to bring out a thermometer easily carried in the pocket. The doctor made his own notes of what the readings meant, and on a slip of paper recorded "97 degrees Subnormal, 98.6 degrees Normal," and so on to "107 degrees . . . Fatal." The microscope was being increasingly used, though the findings laboriously recorded are obscure and meaningless to us. Here, too, we can see some of the first tentative gropings towards the use of "the vapour of chloroform." Its use was not yet a matter of routine. Thus, in one of the cases, although the man underwent three operations within a few days— the third being an amputation through the middle of the thigh—no anæsthetic was given, and the note reads, "bore the operation without complaint." But in another case "the vapour of chloroform was administered and the influence maintained during the greater part of the operation, so

THE FEVER HOSPITAL AND ROYAL INFIRMARY, GLASGOW
Engraving by David Allan, *c.* 1832

that the patient felt little pain." Half an hour after the operation two grains of solid opium were administered.

The cause of death after operation—when indeed it was not due to delay in operating—was nearly always some form of sepsis. Hands and instruments contaminated by one sore were used to examine the wound of the next patient. In 1860 Lister had moved from Edinburgh to Glasgow. He had visited many continental medical schools, and applied himself vigorously to the solution by experiment of one problem after another. He had pondered much on the state of affairs in surgery and had reached the conclusion, which he taught in his lectures, that suppuration was caused by putrefaction or decomposition, which was set up by exposure of the wound to the air, or by other contamination of it. A simple fracture, when the skin was not broken, did not suppurate; when the skin was broken, it did. He determined to try to stop putrefaction in wounds, and chose crude carbolic acid which he knew as a disinfectant of sewage. This he first used in the Glasgow Royal Infirmary in 1865. It was successful, and Lister observed: "So it may fairly be said that the result at the end of the usual time of treatment for a simple fracture was in no way affected by its being compound."

These great events had their antecedents: the medical advances were but the coping stones laid upon work done, mainly in America, on the use of anæsthetics, and on antiseptics by Pasteur in France. In nursing, too, Miss Nightingale was not without foundations upon which to build. There had been a revival of nursing as a vocation for a "Protestant Sister of Charity," and an Anglican nursing sisterhood had been established in 1843 under the influence of Pusey and Keble. King's College Hospital was already staffed by a nursing order which supplied six of the nurses who went to the Crimea.

Florence Nightingale devoted the five years following the war to the health of the British Army ; then she turned to the hospitals and nursing. Her *Notes on Hospitals* of 1859 traced back the excessive mortality to the general defects of the site, the number maintained under a single roof, deficiency of ventilation and of light. She wrote of the necessity of *iron* bedsteads, *hair* mattresses and *glass* or *earthenware* cups (instead of tin). She advocated a system of pavilions in hospital construction. Her principles commanded the support of the better medical opinion, and her detailed advice drawn from observation in the best foreign hospitals was embodied in the design of numerous hospitals up and down the country. St. Thomas's Hospital in Southwark lay in the path of the extension of the Southern Railway from London Bridge to Charing Cross, and its removal to the present site opposite the Houses of Parliament provided an opportunity on a grand scale for the new layout. The present range of "pavilions" was built under Miss Nightingale's inspiration and has proved so satisfactory that no radical change is considered necessary by expert opinion to-day.

She was indefatigable : she was the pioneer of hospital statistics in this country and compared the absence of any uniformity in the hospitals in the publication of their reports to astronomical observations made without concert and reduced to no common standard. Her model Hospital Statistical Forms were adopted by a congress in London, and the leading hospitals were persuaded to publish annually statistics of patients treated, and to adopt her forms as far as practicable. The project was only a partial success. It was in part achieved by the tables compiled thirty years later by Sir Henry Burdett, which were themselves to be the foundation of the statistical returns which have been required by King Edward's Hospital Fund for the last fifty years. The effective comparative assessment of the results obtained in different hospitals remains to-day an ideal yet to be achieved.

Her influence on the standard of nursing was, as all the world knows, immense. The Nightingale Fund, raised by public subscription throughout the Empire and amounting to £44,000, enabled her to establish "an institution for the training, assistance and protection of nurses and hospital attendants." Her choice fell on St. Thomas's Hospital where her friend Mrs. Wardroper was Matron, and had already weeded out the inefficient and obtained "better women" as nurses, though training as such was non-existent. In June 1860, the first fifteen probationers were admitted for a year's training in the Nightingale School. The essential principles were

FLORENCE NIGHTINGALE

Water colour by J. Barrett, 1856

two: "(1) that nurses should have their training in hospitals specially organised for the purpose : (2) that they should live in a home fit to form their moral life and discipline." The Matron filled in the "Monthly Sheet of Personal Character and Acquirements of each Nurse." The School was described in a magazine : "the nurses wore a brown dress and their snowy caps and aprons looked like bits of extra light as they moved cheerfully and noiselessly from bed to bed." From the medical staff alone came criticism ; and the senior surgeon at the hospital was able to write that it was beyond doubt that the hospital-nurse training scheme had not met with the approbation or support of the medical profession. It should not be supposed that the reform of hospital nursing by Miss Nightingale was achieved once and for all in the heroic days of the Crimea. She was throughout the latter part of her life confined to her room, and unable to visit in person her school at St. Thomas's. She lived on till 1910.

The foundation of the Nightingale School powerfully reinforced a contemporary movement for the reform of the Poor Law Infirmaries. The first "workhouse" had been erected at Bristol in 1697. In 1723 a general Act was passed empowering parishes to unite in "unions" for the purpose of building workhouses. By 1732 only a hundred and fifteen had been built of which fifty were in London, and only one in Scotland. In them were usually provided quarters for inmates who fell sick, but the intention was that those who seriously required medical treatment should "if possible" be removed to a hospital. Authority was complacent, a Select Committee on medical relief reporting in 1864 "that the poor were never so promptly attended to or so efficiently relieved during sickness as they are at present." A year later an investigation was instituted by the *Lancet* which exposed the state of neglect in the workhouses. It compared them with the voluntary hospitals and spoke of "a scandalous inequality in our treatment of two classes of sick poor." The country had "allowed a number of establishments to grow up in the external semblance of hospitals for paupers," yet "in truth the whole process is a sham and mere simulacrum of real hospital accommodation." Dr. Joseph Rogers, who was employed by the Strand Board of Guardians, played a prominent part in agitating for improvements.

Meanwhile the example of the Nightingale School had been followed in Liverpool at the Royal Infirmary, and a Nightingale nurse with twelve trained nurses under her had been put in charge of the male wards of the Workhouse Infirmary there with twelve hundred inmates. Miss Agnes Jones—rich, young and witty and intensely religious, "ideal in her beauty, like a Louis XIV shepherdess," found herself in wards which she described as resembling Dante's Inferno. The men wore the same shirts for seven weeks, bedclothes were sometimes not washed for months, the food was appalling, and the lack of morals indescribable. Despite opposition and friction, she got her way, amused by the technique she employed : "she suggests things, she is laughed at. She persists. A decent interval is allowed to elapse : and then the things are suggested to her by the officials. She says the suggestions are excellent.'' Miss Nightingale was not only pleased, but was furnished with the ammunition she needed for representations to the President of the Poor Law Board. An alliance was forged with Mr. Farnall, the Poor Law Inspector for the Metropolitan District. A plan was drawn up—"to insist on the great principles of separating the Sick, Insane, 'Incurable,' and above all, children from the usual population of the Metropolis; to advocate a single central administration; and to provide for a 'General Hospital rate' to be levied over the whole Metropolitan area.'' The Act of 1867 which made provision for Poor Law Infirmaries absolutely separate from the workhouse, and in no sort of way subject to the work-house master, dominated subsequent legislation until the transfer of the responsibility to the local authorities in 1929. The new infirmaries were to have a resident medical superintendent. It was not all that Miss Nightingale wanted—"This is a beginning ; we shall get more in time,'' was her pro-phetic comment.

LEICESTER ROYAL INFIRMARY
Coloured lithograph by H. Walter after Harvey and King. Nineteenth century

THE TURN OF THE CENTURY

RELEASED from their ancient handicaps by the threefold advance—in anæsthetics, in antiseptics and in nursing—the hospitals expanded rapidly during the latter years of the nineteenth century. The practice of medicine had at long last been freed by the discovery of bacterial infection. It was a period of ferment unparalleled since the scientific enlightenment of the seventeenth century. Dysentery, leprosy, typhoid, malaria, cholera, diphtheria, tetanus and plague were yielding up their secrets: the range of surgery had been vastly extended and different specialities were springing up overnight. The early electrical departments were developing photography by X-ray. A young Canadian doctor, William Osler, provided the medical profession in his *Principles and Practice of Medicine* with a guide which opened the doors to this new world—a book of which a hundred thousand copies had been sold within twenty years.

There was a demand for a better organisation of the medical schools, and for the laboratories needed for the application of new discoveries. Patients flocked to the hospitals as never before : especially they came to the larger hospitals in the great cities as transport facilities were improved. The general hospitals extended and set up special departments. Five new teaching hospitals had been established in the earlier part of the nineteenth century in London—Charing Cross, The Royal Free, University College Hospital, King's College Hospital, and St. Mary's—and had greatly increased the facilities for medical education in the capital. By the end of the century all were important units. The special hospitals were also by this time numerous. Most of them owed their origin to medical men anxious to collect together in one hospital a class of patient whose treatment they felt to be neglected in the general hospitals. The Royal London Ophthalmic ("Moorfields") dates back to the early years of the century. The Royal National Orthopædic Hospital had been founded in 1839 by Dr. W. J. Little, the Cancer Hospital by Dr. William Marsden in 1851, the Hospital for Sick Children ("Great Ormond Street") by Dr. Charles West in 1852 and the Royal Hospital for Incurables, Putney, by Dr. Andrew Reed in 1854. At the end of the century such hospitals had become an important part of the hospital system. They afforded a meeting place for the medical men from different schools to mix and learn from one another and they can claim to have pioneered in many directions.

The first cottage hospital was founded at Cranleigh in Surrey in 1859, and by the end of the century cottage hospitals were spreading all over the country. Many of them developed into hospitals of some size and considerable local importance, and indeed the majority of the existing voluntary hospitals outside London and the great cities date from the seventies, eighties and nineties of the last century. The money was found by public subscription. Festival dinners were numerous and successful, and Hospital Sunday and

Hospital Saturday Funds were organised in many parts of the country. Treatment remained free, except in so far as it was controlled by a system of "letters" given by subscribers to patients in whom they were interested. In this respect, American hospitals diverged from our own ; a system of payment by patients there provided a substantial revenue to the hospitals.

There were abuses and the Charity Organisation Society began to turn a critical eye upon the work of the out-patients' departments of the London hospitals. "What more glaring picture of charitable impotence is there," wrote its Secretary, Sir Charles Loch, "than that destitute persons should constantly apply to a free dispensary for drugs which cannot benefit them if they lack the necessary food ?" It was necessary that "medical charity" should act in alliance with "general charity" and he proceeded to outline as a more effectual method the appointment of "assessors," whose purpose would be to secure the general assistance without which medical relief would often fail of its purpose. A new word was wanted and Loch adopted the term "almoner" which had in the early days of St. Bartholomew's and St. Thomas's signified those charged with the duty of examining all persons brought to the hospitals and admitting them at discretion. One winter morning in 1895 Miss Mary Stewart began her work as the first almoner at the Royal Free Hospital in a small screened-off corner of the Out-Patients' Department. This shy diffident lady confronting the crowded benches before her was expected not only to prevent abuse of the hospital by persons able to pay for medical treatment, but, as it were by an after-thought, to meet another need—to be the means whereby "needy and deserving" patients could be followed up after treatment. It was an after-thought destined in our day finally to establish its supremacy over the original conception. From these beginnings there grew in due time a distinct professional organisation and a new conception of the hospital's duty.

In the nineties the expansion of the London hospitals was followed by a series of financial crises. The House of Lords appointed a Committee which sat for three years, and finally issued recommendations which have a curiously modern note. It spoke of a central board to be representative of all the hospitals in London, which should among other things examine proposals for all new hospitals, and advise upon systems of treatment for out-patients. Sir Henry Burdett applied his fertile mind to these problems, and poured out suggestions. His huge four-volume work on *Hospitals and Asylums of the World* contained a mass of information culled from every quarter of the globe. His Hospital Annual did not hesitate to make frank criticisms of individual hospitals. "The Infirmary at . . . at the present time is unworthy, inadequate and altogether inefficient . . ." He dealt too with the needs of the chronic sick—"a good library, pleasant rooms well supplied with games and bright with flowers are almost a *sine qua non*. Each ward should have a large piazza under which the patients may be wheeled and others may sit and recline. . ."

THE HOSPITAL FOR SICK CHILDREN, GREAT ORMOND STREET
Engraving from the *Illustrated Times*, 1858

The great hospitals of London were his special concern. In 1897 Sir Henry succeeded in persuading the Prince of Wales to accept his scheme for a central hospital fund for the Metropolis, as a means of commemorating Queen Victoria's Diamond Jubilee. The Prince devoted his characteristic energy to the scheme—"a project lying very near my heart"—and personally invited contributions from his friends and acquaintances. What later became King Edward's Hospital Fund was thus established, with the twin objects of building up a permanent invested fund and of requiring efficiency in organisation and equipment from hospitals receiving grants. It was an era of isolation. The King's Fund, as it soon came to be called, marked the first stage of the breakdown of this isolation and opened the way to a pooling of ideas. The London Hospital was, for example, encouraged to spend £100,000 of its own invested funds in bringing its equipment up to date in return for an annual grant of £5,000 a year from the Fund.

The stage was set for a further period of expansion of the voluntary hospitals. They stood high in the public estimation; despite the crowding and the waiting lists, there existed among the patients a heartfelt gratitude for the treatment they received and could get nowhere else. Abhorrence of the Poor Law was reinforced by an administration that often failed to keep pace with medical progress, and to maintain the constant supervision over simple matters, such as food and clothing, that is necessary if an institution is not to drift into a backwater in the course of years. The contrast between the two systems as then exemplified was reinforced by memories of the Nightingale exposures of "officialism." "Anything more opposed to the best interests of the people," wrote Burdett, "than the substitution of State hospitals for the voluntary hospitals as they at present exist cannot be imagined. . . . We believe and hope therefore that the day is far distant when any serious effort will be made to substitute State hospitals for the noble medical charities scattered throughout England, charities which are at one and the same time the wonder of foreigners, and the just glory and pride of the British nation."

Such was the opinion of the leading authority on hospitals of his generation. As the decades have passed since 1900 the form of the equation set by the opposing systems of hospital organisation has changed almost beyond recognition. The gulf between the two types of hospital has narrowed, and new conceptions have been born of the need to embrace the various units in a single plan.

ST. THOMAS'S HOSPITAL IN WAR-TIME
Detail from an oil painting by Evelyn Dunbar, 1942

THE IMPACT OF SCIENCE UPON THE HOSPITALS

FIFTY years ago the organisation of even a great hospital was still relatively a simple matter, but the impact of science upon medicine soon became more pronounced. The laboratory was available to supplement diagnosis at the bedside and examination of the body after death. The new approach permitted the study of the chemistry of the living body and the detection of early departures from the normal before pathological changes were recognisable. Bedside medicine was further reinforced by the progress made in physics and the greatly extended use of X-rays, and the electro-cardiograph opened up a fresh approach to the disorders of the circulation. The value of heat, light, massage and graduated exercises was now appreciated, and some attention was paid to the care of the patient after discharge from hospital. These advances carried many implications for the hospitals.

Within living memory there has been so vast an expansion of the hospitals and development has fanned out in so many directions that it ceases to be practicable to touch upon individual hospitals or even to notice the divergent tendencies which have created new types, many of them of intense interest. The building or rebuilding of great hospitals like the Aberdeen Royal Infirmary, the Queen Elizabeth, Birmingham, the Middlesex and the Westminster in London; the provision of hospitals and sanatoria for the treatment of tuberculosis; the development of psychological medicine and neurology and their effect upon the treatment of mental illness; the new approach to rehabilitation, the new technique of plastic surgery; all these and many other developments must be passed over if the central thread is not to disappear in a mass of detail. All in all the number of beds provided has more than doubled in the last fifty years.

The cost has risen dramatically. From £2 per bed per week it has risen first to £3, then to £4. During the war there has been a further steep rise from £5 or £6 a week to £10 or £12 a week in a London teaching hospital. The change reflects in part rising prices and higher wages to all employed in the hospitals, but in the main flows from the increasing complexity of hospital organisation.

Medical schools had long replaced the old privately owned schools of anatomy and surgery. Early in the twentieth century many of these schools were incorporated in the medical faculties of the Universities. The range of scientific knowledge required of the medical student widened; so much so that to-day the emphasis is being placed decisively on grasp of the scientific method rather than on a knowledge of its detailed application. Large sums of public money have been made available to the medical schools, and many further developments—including the removal of all financial barriers that have stood in the way of a medical career—are now projected.

Nursing has been for some years past, and is still to-day, the subject of much controversy. Miss Nightingale's example, and the power of a personality that would have made its mark in any sphere, set a standard in this country which soon became the envy of the world. Nurses were trained to become leaders and pioneers, and for many years nursing enjoyed a prestige which sometimes seems to be in danger of passing away. State Registration came in 1919 ; central examinations were instituted under the General Nursing Council, but the provision of nurses' training schools remained a matter for the hospitals.

It may well be that Miss Nightingale's influence has delayed changes needed to bring rules and regulations into line with modern conceptions and perhaps also that State Registration has led to an excessive emphasis upon examinations. Public discussion has been focused on conditions and culminated in the report of a Working Party in 1947 with a strong emphasis on wastage during training. The conditions under which the nurse works have changed greatly in recent years; fees for training have been abolished, the nurse's health is safeguarded by routine medical examinations, and restrictions on her in off-duty time have largely disappeared. The Nursing Recruitment Service, founded by King Edward's Hospital Fund for London in 1940, is constantly in touch with a large number of those entering hospital for training. Such contact shows over and over again that improvements in material conditions are not the whole story. Throughout history the love of the chance of caring for the sick has ever been the main incentive, and changes in the training and conditions of work in accordance with the trend of the times can never obscure the real nature of the work, for the rewards of nursing lie in the deep satisfaction that the work gives, and in an increasing sense of responsibility for the care of the patients. The numbers entering and qualifying have risen steadily and indeed dramatically for the last twenty years, but the shortening of hours and higher ratios of nurses to patients have outstripped the supply. Though the famous hospitals still have long waiting lists, the fact remains that many more nurses are needed if the whole future of the hospital service is not to be gravely handicapped.

Since the war of 1914-18 it has been customary to ask patients to contribute towards the cost of their treatment, and the task has fallen upon the almoners. Although this work has been greatly simplified by the development of contributory schemes, too much of the almoner's time has often been taken up with this uncongenial task, from which she is released by the new Act which makes hospital treatment free to all. The training of the almoners for their work is a serious matter: a university degree or a course of study in social science is normally required, and is followed by a period of apprenticeship in hospital under the supervision of a trained almoner.

A whole group of new occupations have been born, many of which make a wide appeal. The recognition within quite recent years of the influence

AN OPERATION IN PROGRESS AT ST. MARY'S HOSPITAL, LONDON

Oil painting by Anna Zinkeisen, 1943

STAFF OF THE MIDDLESEX HOSPITAL, MAY 10TH, 1941
Wash drawing by Feliks Topolski

of right feeding upon recovery is leading to a great increase in the demand for dieticians and for catering officers who can bring to the work in hospitals a background of practical experience gained elsewhere. Physiotherapists, or masseuses as they used to be called, occupy important positions in almost every hospital. Fees are charged for training in the schools of massage attached to the hospitals, and there is no lack of candidates for this strenuous and exacting work. Radiography is splitting into two branches, diagnostic and therapeutic; the one concerned with the mechanics of the photographic processes in the X-ray department, and the other with the management of the patients undergoing deep X-ray or radium treatment for cancer and certain other conditions.

The responsibility of the administrator has increased in proportion to the complication of the work. A generation ago the lay management of a hospital might be compared with that of a large private household, and specialised knowledge was of secondary importance. The hospital administrator—whether a layman as has been traditional in most of the voluntary hospitals, or a medical superintendent as in local-authority practice—needs a thorough understanding of the needs of all departments, and must keep abreast of developments in many different directions which may at first sight seem remote from his own sphere.

Here too we must touch upon some of the changes which have led to the nationalisation of the hospitals. From 1900 onwards, although the voluntary hospitals have expanded and multiplied, there had been an increasing overflow of patients into the public hospitals, which continued to be administered under the Poor Law. Its deficiencies were laid bare by the work of Sidney and Beatrice Webb. Improvements were effected by the Metropolitan Asylums Board and other authorities, and after the war of 1914-18 the city of Bradford led the way by providing an up-to-date hospital in which the Poor Law played no part. Nevertheless the general standard left much to be desired.

In 1919 the Local Government Board was re-named the Ministry of Health, and in 1920 there appeared a report inspired by Lord Dawson of Penn in which was sketched out something wholly new, a definite plan for an organised medical service in which general practitioners would be linked in Health Centres, and Health Centres in turn to the hospitals. This report, now all but forgotten, became a guiding star in many parts of the world. Its realisation at home has been slow, and as yet partial, but the principles it enunciated have been embodied in the National Health Service Act of 1946. The first step needed was the release of municipal hospitals from the provisions of the Poor Law and gradually the Ministry of Health resolved to transfer them from the Guardians to the County and County Borough Councils.

The transfer was made by the Local Government Act of 1929. But the high hopes of a new era were only in part realised. Many of the more prosperous urban areas made great strides in bringing the old infirmaries up to a standard comparable to that of the better voluntary hospitals. Much was spent on improvements; equipment was brought up to date; and, above all, resident medical and nursing staffs were raised to a level undreamed of by the Guardians. But other areas lagged behind, and continued to provide only Poor Law accommodation. Despite the equalising effect of subsidies from the Exchequer, the poorer areas proved quite unable to face the expense of building new hospitals or modernising the old. It was already, therefore, apparent before the war that the time had come for a fresh attempt to weld together the voluntary and local authority hospitals into the single system envisaged in Lord Dawson's report.

When war came the prospect of casualties on a great scale meant that a national service had to be improvised, sufficiently elastic to admit of transference of cases from one hospital to another, and in the last few months before the war the hospitals were grouped together in the Emergency Hospital Service. Doctors, matrons and administrators were drawn from the different units and given a quasi-military status in their respective areas. In London and the Home Counties a great re-shuffle took place, involving the creation of Sectors with headquarters in teaching hospitals in London, and branches radiating far out into the country like slices of a cake. When the first casualties arrived from Dunkirk in 1940 and later throughout the air-raids, the system worked smoothly, and it was recognised that many of the elements of the improvisation ought to be embodied in a permanent structure.

The Ministry of Health then took a momentous step by appointing surveyors charged with the duty of making, for the first time in hospital history, detailed recommendations upon the different areas. Everywhere the existing services were found to be capable of vast improvement. Expansion was overdue, and the standard of work was often suffering from a time-lag in the spread of new techniques. The best work was far too often confined to the University cities with their teaching hospitals and numerous consultants, and means had to be found of extending this influence throughout all the hospitals. Some form of regionalisation was clearly essential. Moreover, the provision made for the chronic sick was often sadly inadequate. Their segregation in institutions divorced from the central stream of progress had left them in a backwater unworthy of our present conception of hospital provision. The cost of the reforms needed would be on a scale which could only be found from the Exchequer.

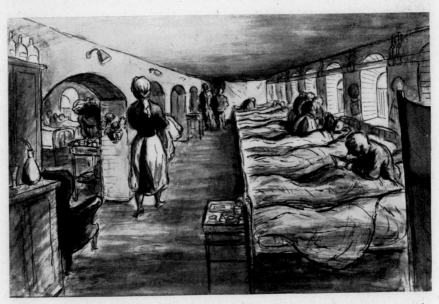

BASEMENT WARD AT THE ROYAL HERBERT HOSPITAL, WOOLWICH
Water colour by Edward Ardizzone, 1940

45

THE ASSUMPTION OF RESPONSIBILITY
BY THE STATE

COULD this great series of reforms be achieved under the dual system of administration? Could the voluntary hospitals retain their independence with its undisputed merits of freedom and initiative and the great popular interest that the contributory schemes enlisted in their support? The Coalition Government was disposed to think that it could be done, and attempted to devise such a system. The Labour Government, returned to power in 1945, decided upon a more radical solution. The National Health Service Act of 1946 provided for outright nationalisation of all the hospitals in England and Wales under the Ministry of Health, and was followed by a similar Act for Scotland.

A few words must suffice to describe the salient features of the scheme. The teaching hospitals are accorded a privileged status. Though technically transferred to the Minister, they retain much of their former freedom. They have their own Boards of Governors, and they retain at their own free disposal the income from their ancient endowments. There are twelve in London with undergraduate medical schools: Charing Cross, Guy's, King's College, the London, the Middlesex, the Royal Free, St. Bartholomew's, St. George's, St. Mary's, St. Thomas's, University College and the Westminster. In the great cities of the provinces there are ten: the Queen Elizabeth at Birmingham, Bristol Royal, Addenbrooke's at Cambridge, the General Infirmary at Leeds, the Royal Liverpool United Hospital, the Royal Victoria Infirmary at Newcastle, the Radcliffe Infirmary at Oxford, and the Royal Infirmaries at Cardiff, Manchester and Sheffield. In Scotland, where the arrangements governing the teaching hospitals are rather different, there are six: the Royal Infirmaries at Aberdeen, Dundee, Edinburgh and Glasgow, and the Victoria and Western Infirmaries at Glasgow. There is to be a great development of postgraduate education for doctors. The British Postgraduate School at Hammersmith Hospital is to be reorganised, and the special hospitals will play their part and rank as teaching hospitals. Many, too, of the larger general hospitals up and down the country will provide refresher courses for general practitioners.

All other hospitals, whether voluntary or administered by the County Councils, pass to the control of Regional Boards appointed by the Minister. They are grouped in units large enough in many cases to include most of the special departments essential to a complete hospital service. Each of these units has a Hospital Management Committee, and is allotted a round sum sufficient to meet its estimated requirements. The Hospital Management Committees are free to spend this as they choose. The reconciliation of the conflicting claims of economy with the demands made by the medical staff for ever-increasing facilities is no simple matter, and calls for qualities of leadership and patience.

NIGHT NURSE
Oil painting by Anna Zinkeisen, 1945

The endowments of the voluntary hospitals other than the teaching hospitals have been transferred to a Hospital Endowments Fund, the income from which will be used for purposes outside the official budget. The hospitals are free to accept gifts; they have, as it were, two pockets, one replenished by the Exchequer, and the other not so. This is a provision of historic importance, which links the future with the past. It is a plan which bids fair to make the best of both worlds, and it is pertinent to recall that away back at the very beginning of the voluntary hospital movement its early protagonist, John Bellers, the Quaker, was in 1714 advocating that "the major part of the expense should be borne by the State, and the minor

47

by voluntary contributions." The great hospital trusts—King Edward's Hospital Fund for London and the Nuffield Provincial Hospitals Trust and Nuffield Foundation—will use their resources to encourage initiative and to help those hospitals which might otherwise lag behind, to keep abreast of progress. If the history of the past is any guide to the future there will not be wanting a steady stream of benevolence flowing towards the hospitals, humanising them and ensuring that they never become mere institutions maintained by the State.

There are many who have supported the voluntary hospitals in the past who feel that something precious will have passed away. It is important therefore to be clear how far essentials can be retained under the new system. We have touched already upon the method of finance. Organisation and staffing are of equal if not of greater importance, and merit a brief discussion in even a cursory survey.

First, the voluntary hospital has traditionally been governed by a body solely concerned with the work of the hospital. Its members have had no occasion to glance over their shoulders at some other body—a government department or a local authority—whose interests they may also have to take into account. "The governing body," wrote Mr. Aleck Bourne, "rides the personnel with so light a rein that it is not felt, and the freedom from office control is the chief source of the freedom and independence of thought which has nursed the spirit of enquiry and research." This is a thing which can very easily be undermined. If, for example, the Hospital Management Committees were to find decisions more and more taken out of their hands by the Regional Boards, we should have to look elsewhere for initiative and progress.

Secondly, there is the part played by the medical staff. The hospital is not to be confused with the governing body alone. It, the hospital, *is* the combination of those two components working upon and influencing each other. The Medical Committee is composed, as a general rule, of all the senior staff. In a large hospital, some thirty, forty or fifty men may sit upon this Committee. It is their duty to keep their colleagues informed of any new equipment or development of knowledge wherever it may occur all over the world ; and some of them sit on the Management Committee and try to convince the Committee that this or that should be done. The arrangement serves a double purpose. It is a guarantee that new projects (and they are legion) before reaching the governing body have first run the gauntlet of criticism and discussion in the Medical Committee : and it sets the governing body itself free from the futility of spending its time listening to endless debates among the medical men.

Thirdly, there is the important principle which governs the actual staffing. The historic practice evolved in the voluntary hospitals is for the responsible medical work to be entrusted to a number of part-time honoraries, who jointly comprise the medical staff of the hospital. Each has a group of beds for which he is held responsible. His initial appointment and subsequent career are dependent on the estimate of his ability formed by his colleagues and equals, and, in teaching hospitals, on the opinion of his students. If his students approve of him, they in their turn will later send their difficult cases to him for consultation.

In the new Act little or no reference is made to these things, which are characteristic of the hospitals of the English-speaking peoples. Their importance is certainly appreciated by the Ministry of Health, and there is every reason to expect that the new hospital service will provide freedom from interference from the Hospital Management Committees, and ample scope for medical staff committees in all hospitals.

Another tradition, however, which we inherit from the past is wholly bad. Since the suppression of the monasteries, the care of the incurable or chronic sick has been largely divorced from the main stream of work in the voluntary general hospitals. The voluntary hospitals of the eighteenth century were founded not to "care" for the sick but to cater for those capable of "cure" by Physick and Surgery. It was a necessary limitation if the hospitals were not to degenerate into mere almshouses. But now we have come full circle and the hospitals, with the State resources behind them, must be made strong enough to shoulder the burden. This does not mean that the hospitals for the acute sick with all their special departments should open their doors to all and sundry, for that would be to waste their facilities. But the grouping of all hospitals into larger units will unify the medical and nursing staffs of the acute and chronic hospitals, from which the latter will reap great benefit. The ending of the divorce between the acute and chronic sick will, we can confidently expect, prove to be one of the greatest achievements of the present reforms. It will be a return, at least in part, to the mediæval conception of a hospital as a home for all who need it, as well as a centre where doctors and surgeons deal with those within their power to cure.

The new statute guarantees the organisation, the finance, and a certain standard of efficiency in the services provided. But just as in the past the Education Acts have proved only partially successful at the point where the human factor comes most into play, so in carrying out the National Health Service Act the quality of the service will finally depend upon factors which lie outside the scope of legislation.

It may be that we are now entering upon a phase in which the vigorous application of preventive medicine and social hygiene will progressively lighten the burden on the hospitals, and statisticians will watch with interest its effect upon hospital records.

Our own day will surely go down in history as an era of discoveries almost as momentous as any in the past. The development of blood transfusion, the use of the sulphanilamide group of drugs, and the already famous discovery of penicillin by Sir Almroth Wright and Sir Alexander Fleming

49

at St. Mary's Hospital in association with Sir Howard Florey at Oxford have not yet operated to reduce the demand for hospital beds. But the omens for the future are good. Throughout the hospital service there is a determination to see that, so far as is humanly possible, all that is best in the past shall be carried over into the future, and that the elements of profound value in the tradition which we have traced shall continue to fertilise the whole range of our hospital services.

"The sentiment awakened by the hospitals," wrote Burdett, "is a living force in the hearts of English men and women. It needs no awakening by fine writing or eloquence." The words are as true to-day as they have been for centuries past.

SHORT BIBLIOGRAPHY

For the early period the reader may be referred to *Mediæval Hospitals* by R. M. Clay, 1909. For the rest the story has to be pieced together from the records of the individual hospitals, among which may be specially mentioned : *The History of St. Bartholomew's Hospital* by Sir Norman Moore, 2 vols., 1918 ; *The History of St. Thomas's Hospital* by F. G. Parsons, 3 vols., 1932-36 ; *The Royal Infirmary of Edinburgh 1729-1929* by A. Logan Turner, 1937 ; and a shorter book, *A History of the London Hospital* by Sir Ernest Morris, 3rd ed. 1926. The most recent is *A History of the Worcester Royal Infirmary* by W. H. McMenemey, 1947.

Sir Henry Burdett's four-volume *Hospitals and Asylums of the World*, 1893, is a mine of information, but is not generally accessible. *The Life of Florence Nightingale* by Sir E. T. Cook, 2 vols., 1913, is indispensable to an understanding of the nineteenth century and is eminently readable.

Ives, Arthur G. L.   WZ70
British hospitals   I95b

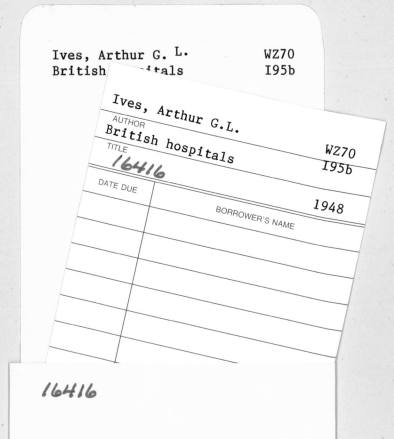

Ives, Arthur G.L.

AUTHOR
British hospitals   WZ70
TITLE   I95b
16416

DATE DUE	BORROWER'S NAME	1948

16416